STAR WARS
JEDI

CONTENTS

Published by Pedigree Books Limited
Beech Hill House, Walnut Gardens, Exeter, Devon EX4 4DH
E-mail books@pedigreegroup.co.uk
Published 2006

WELCOME, YOUNG JEDI

Guardians of peace and justice, the Jedi are. Users of the Force. Jedi Knights embody the utmost sense of virtue, nobility and discipline within the universe. For over 1000 generations, the Jedi Knights have served the Galactic Republic. Maintained order and unity, they have.

MAJOR EVENTS IN YODA'S LIFETIME

YEAR	EVENT
-896	Yoda born
-600	Jabba the Hutt born
-200	Chewbacca born
-102	Count Dooku born
-92	Qui-Gon born
-57	Obi-Wan born
-46	Padmé Amidala born
-44	Obi-Wan becomes a Padawan
-41.9	Anakin Skywalker born
-32.5	Padmé Amidala elected Queen of Naboo
-32	Battle of Naboo
-29	Han Solo born
-28	Anakin builds his lightsaber
-22	Battle of Geonosis

PADAWAN!

-22	Clone Wars begin
-22	Marriage of Anakin and Padmé
-19	Yoda battles Darth Sidious
-19	Luke & Leia born
-19	Yoda goes into hiding on Dagobah System
0	Obi-Wan shows Luke the Force
0	Obi-Wan becomes one with the Force
0	Battle of Yavin
0	Destruction of the Death Star
3	Battle of Hoth
3	Yoda trains Luke on Dagobah
3.5	Boba Fett delivers Han Solo to Jabba
4	Boba Fett falls into the Sarlacc
4	Death of Jabba the Hutt
4	Yoda becomes one with the Force

Yoda

Weapon: Green lightsaber
Height: 0.66 metres
Vehicle: Floating chair, kybuck
Padawan[s]: Ikrit, Luke Skywalker

Master Yoda trained Jedi Knights in the ways of the Force for over 800 years. He taught them the importance of staying calm, passive and at peace. Master Yoda knew that a true Jedi must be aware of the present and mindful of the future, and use the Force only for defence, never for attack. He was small in size, but his skills in the Force were legendary.

Obi-Wan Kenobi

Weapon: Blue lightsaber
Height: 1.79 metres
Vehicle: Jedi starfighter
Master: Qui-Gon Jinn
Padawan[s]: Anakin Skywalker, Luke Skywalker

Obi-Wan Kenobi was a resourceful Jedi Knight who was cautious and disciplined. As a Padawan he could be headstrong, but he was always consistent with the basic Jedi teachings. Quick and agile, he was a bold warrior and completely trustworthy.

Qui-Gon Jinn

Weapon: Green lightsaber
Height: 1.93 metres
Master: Count Dooku
Padawan[s]: Xanatos, Obi-Wan Kenobi

Qui-Gon Jinn was a dedicated Jedi Master. Considered something of a rebel, Qui-Gon was strongly connected to the living Force. He had great compassion and empathy for other living things, and he was considered by all to be noble and wise. He was an accomplished warrior and wielded his lightsaber with grace and skill.

Padmé Amidala

Weapon: Royal pistol
Height: 1.65 metres
Vehicle: Naboo royal cruiser

Padmé Amidala longed for a peaceful resolution to the civil strife plaguing the Republic. Her outspoken nature shone as a beacon of reason and rationality in the Senate. When the Separatist movement arose, she was one of the few championing a peaceful resolution to the crisis. Padmé was greatly loved by the people of her home planet, Naboo.

Mace Windu

Weapon: Purple lightsaber
Height: 1.88 metres
Padawan(s): Depa Billaba, Echuu Shen-Jon

Calm and controlled, Mace Windu was a noble member of the Jedi High Council. He was a highly revered Jedi Master who was a diplomat by nature. He preferred to seek peaceful solutions to the most difficult issues. However, when called upon to fight, he was a fearsome warrior and was never afraid to face danger.

Anakin Skywalker

Weapon: Blue lightsaber
Height: 1.85 metres
Vehicle: Jedi starfighter
Master: Obi-Wan Kenobi

Born a slave, Anakin Skywalker was mechanically inclined from an early age. As a child he built many devices, including a fully functioning protocol droid named See-Threepio. Strongly connected to the Force, Anakin had the ability to sense events before they happen.
He was brash and daring, and as a Padawan he was at the top of his class in lightsaber training, piloting and memory skills.

Luke Skywalker

Weapon: Blue lightsaber
Height: 1.72 metres
Vehicle: X-wing starfighter
Masters: Obi-Wan Kenobi and Yoda

Luke Skywalker grew up on his uncle's moisture farm. He believed that his father had worked on a spice freighter, never suspecting that Anakin Skywalker was once a Jedi Knight and gifted pilot.

Luke dreamed of joining the Imperial Academy with his best friend Biggs Darklighter, but Luke's uncle always needed him on the farm.

Princess Leia Organa

Weapon: Sporting blaster pistol
Height: 1.5 metres
Vehicle: *Tantive IV*

The beautiful Princess Leia Organa was a symbol of diplomacy, strength, and hope within the Rebel Alliance. Leia was the youngest Senator ever in the Imperial Senate. As such, she ran a number of 'diplomatic aid missions' that were fronts for Rebel re-supply missions. Leia had a strong sense of compassion and a quirky sense of humour.

Han Solo

Weapon: Heavy blaster pistol
Height: 1.8 metres
Vehicle: *Millennium Falcon*

A former smuggler and space pirate, Han Solo was quick thinking and even quicker with a blaster. Han was noted for his narrow escapes from dangerous situations, many of which are the result of his arrogance. His uncanny luck is equalled only by his extraordinary piloting abilities. After winning the *Millennium Falcon* from Lando Calrissian, Han extensively modified it to become one of the fastest space vessels in the galaxy.

Chewbacca

Weapon: Bowcaster
Height: 2.28 metres
Vehicle: *Millennium Falcon*

Chewbacca was a veteran of the Clone Wars, where he served with Yoda, along side fellow Wookiee Tarfful. He later became first mate and co-pilot of the *Millennium Falcon*. Chewbacca was a natural mechanic and over two hundred years old. He communicated in a series of growls, grunts, and fierce roars, and Han Solo was one of the few who understood the Wookiee's native language.

R2-D2 (Artoo-Detoo)

Manufacturer: Industrial automaton
Type: Astromech droid
Weapon: Arc welder, buzz saw
Height: 0.96 metres
Vehicle: Naboo starfighter, X-wing starfighter

The ever-faithful R2-D2 was more than an average astromech droid. This R2 unit had a feisty personality and was very resourceful, which allowed him to save the lives of his friends on numerous occasions. With his counterpart C-3PO, he witnessed some of the key events in the galaxy's history.

C-3PO (See-Threepio)

Manufacturer: Anakin Skywaker
Type: Protocol droid
Height: 1.67 metres

Built by Anakin Skywalker, the protocol droid C-3PO began his existence as a loyal servant to Anakin's mother Shmi. He was always worrying and fussing, and he longed for a quiet life, but somehow he always seems to get involved in adventures! He was rarely seen without his droid companion R2-D2, and they made a great team.

EXCERPTS FROM SEE-THREEPIO'S JOURNAL

YEAR: -32
ENTRY: 1

I am See-Threepio, Human Cyborg relations. I was built by my young and talented Master, Anakin Skywalker. My home is here on Tatooine, which is under the control of the Hutts.

ENTRY: 2

It will take a long time before I am complete, because Master Anakin and his mother Shmi are poor slaves. They belong to a junk dealer called Watto.

Until I get some coverings, my parts have to be on show and I am naked. How embarrassing!

ENTRY: 3

A Jedi Knight called Qui-Gon Jinn has come looking for parts for his ship with a young lady called Miss Padmé. They have a very rude little astromech droid called R2-D2.

Their cruiser's hyperdrive is leaking and they have had to stop to refuel and repair the ship. Space travel sounds rather perilous. Watto has the parts they need, but they have no money.

ENTRY: 4

Master Anakin has told the travellers about the Podracer he built. He is the only human who is quick enough to compete in the dreadful sport. I know that he is a gifted pilot, but I cannot bear to watch!

Master Anakin has offered to help Qui-Gon by entering a Podrace and using the prize money to buy parts. Qui-Gon Jinn is very interested in Master Anakin. It seems that his midi-chlorian count is unusually high.

Qui-Gon has made a deal with Watto. If Master Anakin wins the Podrace, he will be set free. Qui-Gon tried to free Shmi, too, but Watto will not risk losing two slaves.

ENTRY: 6

Vast, cheering crowds are at the arena to see the Podrace. Qui-Gon told Master Anakin not to think, but just to use his instincts. I stood next to Artoo as the gangster Jabba the Hutt started the race.

ENTRY: 7

I feel as if all my circuits are fusing! It has been such an exciting day!

Podracing is very dangerous – many competitors crash and explode into balls of flame. Sebulba, who is a dreadful cheat, tried to knock Anakin out of the race. Oh my goodness, I could hardly believe that he would survive in one piece! But Anakin got into first place on the final lap. Sebulba crashed as Anakin zoomed ahead and won!

ENTRY: 8

Qui-Gon has taken Master Anakin with him to Coruscant, to train him as a Jedi. He found it very hard to say goodbye to his mother. He is my maker, and I wish him well. But I would like it better if I were a little less naked. I hope that Shmi does not sell me while he is away!

YEAR: -22
ENTRY: 1

Master Anakin has returned at last! I can hardly believe it! (I still don't have my outer coverings.) He has brought Miss Padmé with him. He has become a handsome young Jedi, and has learned many things since he left here ten years ago!

I was working outside the Lars homestead, where we have lived since Shmi was sold to Cliegg Lars. He has now freed her and married her, but what a time for Master Anakin to arrive! Shmi has been captured by Tusken Raiders!

Master Anakin has gone to hunt for his mother.

ENTRY: 2

Master Anakin has returned to the Lars homestead with his mother's body. It is a very sad time. He buried her, and he seemed to be filled with grief and anger.

ENTRY: 3

Artoo showed Master Anakin and Miss Padmé a report transmitted from Obi-Wan Kenobi, the Jedi Knight who is teaching Master Anakin. Obi-Wan was attacked halfway through his message! The Jedi Council has ordered Master Anakin not to go looking for Obi-Wan, but Master Anakin was always headstrong.

"I'm going after him!" he cried.

ENTRY: 4

Today I left Tatooine for the first time since I was created. I am travelling to a planet called Geonosis with Master Anakin, Artoo and my new owner, Miss Padmé.

When our starfighter landed on Geonosis, Miss Padmé and Master rushed off to find Obi-Wan. Humans are most confusing. One moment they're generating a pleasant mutual attraction and the next, waves of violent hostility. I don't suppose that I will ever understand them.

ENTRY: 5

Artoo wants to go looking for Master Anakin and Miss Padmé. There have been some very loud noises outside. He keeps saying that they were in danger, which seems very unlikely. This looks like a very dull planet.

ENTRY: 6

That stubborn little droid dragged me into the most frightening adventure I've ever had! Despite the fact that we had been *instructed* to stay behind, he insisted that we left the ship and went looking for trouble. We found a vast droid factory – machines were being built by machines! That nearly made my logic circuits fuse! In my surprise, I fell into the dangerous machinery!

ENTRY: 7

I can hardly believe what has happened. My head was cut from my body! A battle droid head was attached to my body, and my head was welded to a battle droid body!

Outside, the Jedi Knights had arrived to rescue Obi-Wan, Miss Padmé and Master Anakin. A huge battle began between the battle droids and the Jedi's clone troopers…and I was drawn into the fight! Against my will, my separated head and body joined the battle! At last, Artoo rescued me and put me back together. The brave Jedi warriors defeated Count Dooku's army, and Miss Padmé and Master Anakin were safe!

ENTRY: 8

Master Anakin lost his arm in a fight with Count Dooku, and it was replaced with a mechanical one. Artoo and I are now on Miss Padmé's home planet of Naboo. We have come here to witness something very special and very secret. In the late afternoon, by the sparkling lake, Master Anakin and Miss Padmé were married.

YEAR: -19
ENTRY: 1

The Clone Wars have been raging for three years, and these are dark times. Miss Padmé keeps arguing for peace in her role as Senator, and Master Anakin is far away, fighting alongside Master Kenobi. Miss Padmé is pregnant, but she is still keeping her marriage a secret.

ENTRY: 2

General Grievous has kidnapped Supreme Chancellor Palpatine, and Master Kenobi and Master Anakin have gone to rescue him. Poor Miss Padmé is very worried. If only I could do something to help!

ENTRY: 3

Master Kenobi and Master Anakin have rescued Supreme Chancellor Palpatine and Count Dooku is dead, but General Grievous has escaped.

ENTRY: 4

General Grievous has been located on Utapau and Master Kenobi has gone to find him. Many other Jedi Knights are spread out across the galaxy, fighting to restore peace.

ENTRY: 5

There has been a great disturbance at the Jedi Temple – we can see the smoke from Miss Padmé's apartment. We heard no news of Master Anakin for hours, and Miss Padmé was very frightened. But at last we saw his fighter docking on the veranda. Artoo and I are so confused. It seems that the Jedi order has tried to overthrow the Republic, and Master Mace Windu is dead. Many Jedi have been killed. We don't even know if Master Kenobi is alive!

ENTRY: 6 ○

Master Anakin has gone away again. Artoo is worried about him, but he is under a lot of stress. I tried to comfort Miss Padmé, but I feel so helpless!

○ ENTRY: 7

Thank goodness, Master Kenobi is alive. He has terrible news. The Republic has fallen and the Jedi order has been destroyed. He says that Master Anakin has turned to the dark side! He has killed all the younglings in the Temple! Miss Padmé refused to tell Master Kenobi anything. She will not believe that her husband is capable of all those terrible things. She is going to look for him, and she is taking me with her as pilot. Oh dear. I must try to keep her spirits up.

ENTRY: 8 ○

Miss Padmé has found Master Anakin on Mustafar, but Master Kenobi has stowed away on board the Naboo skiff. I watched as Miss Padmé talked to Master Anakin. My maker has changed. Even I can see that he has turned to the dark side! Poor Miss Padmé! She collapsed and now Master Kenobi and Master Anakin are duelling!

○ ENTRY: 9

I lifted Miss Padmé in my arms and carried her into the skiff. At last Master Kenobi returned. Miss Padmé asked if Master Anakin was all right, but she got no answer. She has passed out again. Artoo will watch over her as we go to Polis Massa, where Master Yoda and Bail Organa are waiting.

ENTRY: 10 ○

Palpatine is now the Emperor. Even Master Yoda could not defeat him. Miss Padmé has died giving birth to twins. The little boy, Luke, will go to live with his uncle on Tatooine. The little girl, Leia, will go to live with Bail Organa and his wife. Artoo and I are both going to work for Bail Organa now, but I heard him say that I was to have my memory erased! Oh dear...

THE JEDI ORDER

The Golden Age

In the Golden Age, the Jedi were powerful and numerous. The coming of the Sith changed everything, but some truths still remain, waiting for a hero who will defeat the Sith and create a new Jedi order!

The first Jedi appeared in the Republic 25,000 years before the Battle of Naboo. The order was founded to study philosophy and theology. Eventually, the Jedi learned to understand and control the Force, the powerful energy field that connects all living things.

The earliest Jedi preferred isolation and meditation, but slowly these beliefs changed. The Jedi order began to serve the galactic community. They gradually became a respected and powerful force for good. The order contained representatives from hundreds of species throughout the galaxy. All Jedi served as ambassadors, mediators and counsellors, only resorting to combat when absolutely necessary.

A trained Jedi can tap into and manipulate the Force to accomplish remarkable feats, such as moving objects with the mind, leaping great distances or even sensing the future. The Jedi also became great warriors, using their lightsabers with incredible skill.

The Jedi place great value on self-control and emotional strength. They are patient, honourable and even-tempered. They avoid anger and hate, focusing their energies instead on enlightenment and inner peace. Jedi are born with a strong connection to the Force, but this must be developed by a skilful teacher. The training process is difficult, challenging both the mind and body. When a Padawan has reached a deeper understanding of the Force, they take the Jedi trials. The trials determine whether the Padawan can rise to the rank of Jedi Knight. Eventually, the most talented Jedi Knights become Jedi Masters.

JEDI TECHNOLOGY

Lightsaber

The lightsaber is the weapon of a Jedi, elegant and civilised. In comparison, blasters are primitive, inaccurate and noisy. To carry a lightsaber is an indication of incredible skill, dexterity and attunement to the Force.

When deactivated, a lightsaber appears as a polished metallic handle, about 30cm long and lined with control studs. At the press of a button the energy contained within forms as a shaft of pure energy about a metre long. The saber hums distinctively and its shimmering blade can cut through almost anything, except for the blade of another lightsaber.

In the hands of a Jedi, a lightsaber is almost unstoppable. Using the Force, a Jedi can even predict and deflect incoming blaster bolts. Each Jedi builds his own lightsaber as part of his training.

Jedi Starfighter

Size: (Delta-7) 8 metres long; (Eta-2) 5.47 metres long
Type: Light interceptor starfighter
Weapon: (Delta-7) laser cannons; (Eta-2) 2 laser cannons; 2 secondary ion cannons

These are small, wedge-shaped, one-man starfighters. While the ship does employ weapons, most Jedi pilots prefer to rely on their skill and connection to the Force to avoid conflict.

An astromech droid is hard-wired into the starfighter's port side, providing repair and navigation information to the pilot. The vessel is too small to carry a hyperdrive, and relies on a separate booster craft for travel through hyperspace.

A99 Aquatic Breather

These compact breathing devices allow the wearer to undertake long underwater journeys. The aquatic breather is kept on the Jedi's utility belt. The Jedi Master Qui-Gon Jinn and his Padawan apprentice Obi-Wan Kenobi used them on Naboo when they visited Otoh Gunga, which lay hidden deep beneath a swamp lake.

Training Remote

Training remotes are small, floating spheres that have relatively harmless blasters and an array of sensors. Jedi use remotes to improve their lightsaber skills and their connection to the Force. A Jedi in training wears a vision-obscuring mask and then uses the Force to visualise the remote's location and actions, trying to block any incoming shots. A missed block results in a painful sting.

Comlink

A comlink is a small, hand-held personal communications transceiver. It is a receiver, a transmitter and a small power source. Comlinks vary in size and type, and can be hand-held cylindrical models, flat wrist-mounted units or built in to armoured helmets.

Some comlinks have extra features. The comlink used by Qui-Gon Jinn has a port built into its base for transmitting data.

TO BE A JEDI

There are many steps along the path to becoming a Jedi, and take them you must. Only by following each step can you achieve your goals and become a Jedi Master.

1. PRE-SELECTION

Those who are pre-selected to become Jedi Knights have a high midi-chlorian count. This is detected by a blood test at birth.

2. JEDI HOPEFUL

The Jedi hopefuls are tested for clairvoyant extension of the senses (hearing, touch, sight, taste, smell) over short distances.

3. JEDI CLAN

(Age 4–8)

Jedi reflexes are tested by practising with remotes. Lightsaber skills are improved with sparring practice.

4. ADVANCED TRAINING

(Age 8-9)

In advanced training, the younglings practise and improve their skills in levitation, piloting and controlling bodily functions such as hunger and thirst, and keeping the body warm in extreme cold.

5. BUILD LIGHTSABER

6. CHOSEN TO BECOME A PADAWAN

The few Jedi who are not selected to be a Padawan join the Agricultural Corps.

7. JEDI PADAWAN

(Age: 9–19)

The many and skilful Jedi abilities must be mastered by the young Padawan.

8. JEDI TRIALS

The Padawan must go on an individual mission.

9. JEDI KNIGHT

(Age: 19–25)

After a Padawan has become a Jedi Knight, their advanced skills depend on species or an individual's personal abilities.

10. JEDI MASTER

A Jedi Knight becomes a Master based on past achievements and accomplishments, or when chosen to be a member of the Jedi Council. Usually, those who are elevated to Master have trained a Padawan through to Knighthood.

WORD SEARCH

Now, my young Padawan, time it is to test your skills of observance. Look for these words in the panel below. They are all words that are important to a Jedi. Gain one point for each word you find. The words may be upside down, diagonal or back to front.

Compassion	Honesty
Empathy	Benevolence
Control	Community
Peace	Responsibility
Harmony	Humility

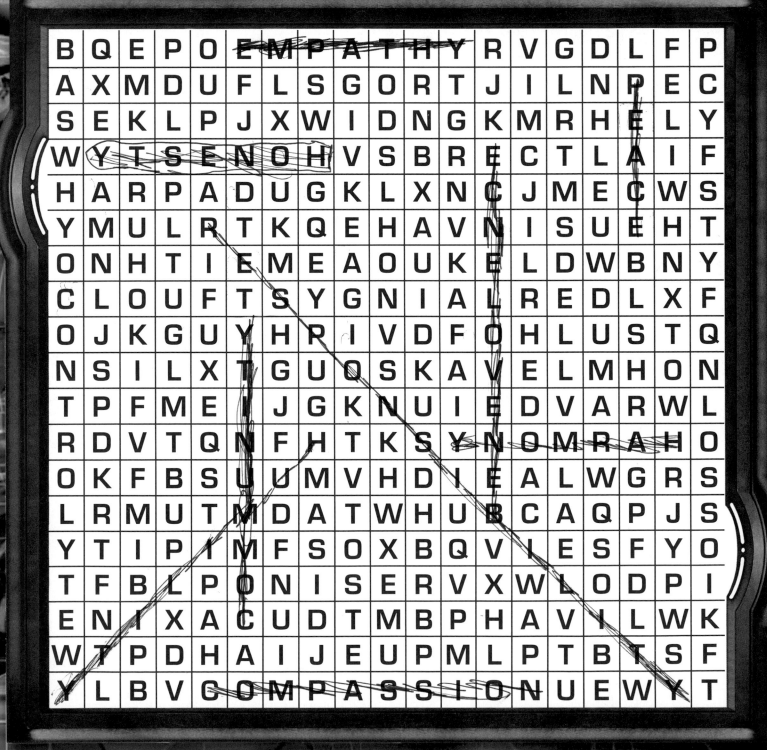

B	Q	E	P	O	E	M	P	A	T	H	Y	R	V	G	D	L	F	P
A	X	M	D	U	F	L	S	G	O	R	T	J	I	L	N	P	E	C
S	E	K	L	P	J	X	W	I	D	N	G	K	M	R	H	E	L	Y
W	Y	T	S	E	N	O	H	V	S	B	R	E	C	T	L	A	I	F
H	A	R	P	A	D	U	G	K	L	X	N	C	J	M	E	C	W	S
Y	M	U	L	R	T	K	Q	E	H	A	V	N	I	S	U	E	H	T
O	N	H	T	I	E	M	E	A	O	U	K	E	L	D	W	B	N	Y
C	L	O	U	F	T	S	Y	G	N	I	A	L	R	E	D	L	X	F
O	J	K	G	U	Y	H	R	I	V	D	F	O	H	L	U	S	T	Q
N	S	I	L	X	T	G	U	O	S	K	A	V	E	L	M	H	O	N
T	P	F	M	E	I	J	G	K	N	U	I	E	D	V	A	R	W	L
R	D	V	T	Q	N	F	H	T	K	S	Y	N	O	M	R	A	H	O
O	K	F	B	S	U	U	M	V	H	D	I	E	A	L	W	G	R	S
L	R	M	U	T	M	D	A	T	W	H	U	B	C	A	Q	P	J	S
Y	T	I	P	I	M	F	S	O	X	B	Q	V	I	E	S	F	Y	O
T	F	B	L	P	O	N	I	S	E	R	V	X	W	L	O	D	P	I
E	N	I	X	A	C	U	D	T	M	B	P	H	A	V	I	L	W	K
W	T	P	D	H	A	I	J	E	U	P	M	L	P	T	B	T	S	F
Y	L	B	V	C	O	M	P	A	S	S	I	O	N	U	E	W	Y	T

YEAR: 0
ENTRY: 1

Artoo and I are with Princess Leia, racing home on her starship, with stolen plans of the Imperial Death Star. How did a Protocol Droid like me ever get involved? We're doomed!

ENTRY: 2

The ship has been captured by Darth Vader and his stormtroopers! Artoo and I have managed to escape. We have landed on a planet called Tatooine.

ENTRY: 3

That malfunctioning little twerp has got us into so much trouble! First we landed in the middle of a huge desert. Then, after walking for kilometres and kilometres, we were captured by Jawas and sold as servants. We seem to be made to suffer.

ENTRY: 4

Our new Master, Luke Skywalker, has been very kind. And how has that naughty astromech droid repaid him? He has run away!

ENTRY: 5

Artoo led us to an old recluse called Obi-Wan Kenobi, who was once a Jedi Knight. He told us that Master Luke's father, Anakin Skywalker, was a Jedi Knight and a great star pilot. Anakin was killed by Darth Vader, who was once Master Kenobi's Padawan pupil!

Artoo played a message from Princess Leia. She begged Master Kenobi to take the plans of the Death Star to her father, Bail Organa, on Alderaan. Artoo has had the plans all along!

ENTRY: 6

Poor Master Luke. His aunt and uncle have been killed by Darth Vader's troops! He has joined Master Kenobi. He wants to become a Jedi Knight, like his father. But first, Master Kenobi must find a ship.

ENTRY: 7

We are at an extremely unpleasant spaceport called Mos Eisley. Master Kenobi has hired a pilot called Han Solo. His first mate is a Wookiee called Chewbacca. They have a ship named the *Millennium Falcon*.

ENTRY: 8

Oh dear, oh dear. The Death Star has destroyed Alderaan and drawn the *Millennium Falcon* in with a tractor beam! We have been captured!

○ ENTRY: 9

Captain Solo and his first mate are obviously used to adventures. First we had to hide from stormtroopers. Then we blasted the Imperial officers in the command office. As Master Luke said, between between Chewbacca's howling and Captain Solo's blasting everything in sight, it's a wonder the whole station doesn't know we're here.

ENTRY: 10 ○

Artoo has located the computer that was powering the tractor beam. If we can disconnect that, we can escape! Master Kenobi has gone to find it. Suddenly Artoo started to beep. Princess Leia is on the ship! Captain Solo, Master Luke and Chewbacca have gone to rescue the Princess, while Artoo and I stay in the command office

ENTRY: 11

Master Luke has rescued Princess Leia, and the tractor beam has been turned off. Now we have to find Master Kenobi and escape!

ENTRY: 12

We raced past stormtroopers and at last reached our ship again. But then we saw Master Kenobi battling Darth Vader! Vader's sword cut the old Jedi Knight in half. But it was most peculiar – Master Kenobi's body disappeared!

ENTRY: 13

After a very scary escape, we have arrived at Yavin 4, the headquarters of the Rebel Alliance. But the Death Star has followed us here – there is going to be a terrible battle!

ENTRY: 14

The Rebels know that the Death Star has a weakness, but the target area is only two metres wide. A precise hit will destroy the entire battle station. Master Luke is piloting a fighter.

ENTRY: 15 ○

Many brave Rebels were shot down, but Master Luke hit the target. The Death Star exploded into millions of tiny, burning pieces! Darth Vader has escaped, but Master Luke and Captain Solo are safe. There is a new hope that the Empire can one day be destroyed.

YEAR: 3
ENTRY: 1

Master Luke has helped establish a new secret base here on the ice world of Hoth. But he has had a vision and must travel to the Dagobah system, to be trained by Master Yoda, the only Jedi Master left alive.

ENTRY: 2

Darth Vader has found our secret base! The Rebel forces are preparing to leave, and Master Luke and Artoo are going to help fight the ground troops before they leave for the Dagobah system. I do hope they take good care of themselves!

ENTRY: 3

Captain Solo, Princess Leia, Chewbacca and I have escaped. But the hyperdrive motivator has been damaged. It's impossible to go to light speed! To escape the fighters, Captain Solo has driven into an asteroid field. But the possibility of successfully navigating an asteroid field is approximately 3,720 to one. (Captain Solo didn't seem to want to hear the odds, though.) Now we are hiding inside a cave on an enormous asteroid. This is suicide!

ENTRY: 4

I talked to the *Falcon* to find out what was wrong with the hyperdrive. (I don't know where this ship learned to communicate, but it has the most peculiar dialect.) The power coupling on the negative axis has been polarised. Captain Solo will have to replace it.

ENTRY: 5

The ship has been repaired – but now there is another danger. There are some strange noises outside. Princess Leia and Captain Solo have gone outside to investigate. I think it might be better if I stay here and guard the ship.

ENTRY: 6

Oh my goodness! We weren't inside a crater at all! We were inside a giant space slug! Thank the maker, we escaped. But now an Imperial Star Destroyer is pursuing us.

⊙ ENTRY: 7

We have escaped and are heading for a planet called Bespin, where a friend of Captain Solo's, Lando Calrissian, may be able to help us.

ENTRY: 8

We have landed on Bespin's Cloud City. Lando Calrissian seemed very friendly, but then something terrible happened. I heard an R2 unit beeping and went to investigate. When I walked into the room, it was filled with stormtroopers! A laser bolt sent me flying in 20 directions at once!

⊙ ENTRY: 9

The next thing I saw was the face of Chewbacca. He was trying to mend me, and I was in pieces. Darth Vader is on Cloud City! He has captured us all and Captain Solo has been tortured. Darth Vader wants us as a trap to catch Master Luke. I have not been completely put back together, so I am strapped to Chewbacca's back. What a ridiculous position to be in!

ENTRY: 10 ⊙

Poor Captain Solo! He has been frozen in carbonite and the bounty hunter Boba Fett is going to take him to Jabba the Hutt. We were being marched to Darth Vader's ship when Lando rescued us! Then I saw my little friend, Artoo. Master Luke has come to help us! We tried to reach Captain Solo and save him, but we were too late. We jumped on board the *Millennium Falcon* and Lando flew us away.

⊙ ENTRY: 11

We had not gone far before Princess Leia made us turn around. Somehow, she knew where Master Luke was and rescued him. He has fought Darth Vader and lost his hand, but he is alive. He is very disturbed – he has discovered that Darth Vader is his father!

YEAR: 4
ENTRY: 1 O

We have returned to Master Luke's home planet of Tatooine to rescue Captain Solo. Artoo and I have been sent to talk to Jabba the Hutt, but I don't think we should rush into all this.

ENTRY: 2

Artoo and I have entered the palace of Jabba the Hutt. I have a bad feeling about this. We were brought before the vile, slobbering Jabba and Artoo played Master Luke's hologram message. He said that he wants to bargain for Captain Solo's life…and that he is giving Artoo and I to Jabba as a gift! Jabba has accepted us – and refused to bargain. We're doomed!

ENTRY: 3

I have been set to work as a translator. Artoo has to work on the Sail Barge. A bounty hunter has arrived, bringing Chewbacca! As I translated Jabba's negotiations for a price, I saw that Lando was there, too, disguised as a skiff guard.

ENTRY: 4

Oh dear, oh dear. The bounty hunter was Princess Leia in disguise! She released Han from the carbonite, but now they are both prisoners, and the Princess is being forced to work as Jabba's slave!

ENTRY: 5

Master Luke arrived and faced Jabba. His training with Master Yoda has turned him into a brave young Jedi. But he is doomed! He and Captain Solo have been condemned to be cast into the pit of Carkoon, the nesting place of the all-powerful Sarlacc!

ENTRY: 6

Thank the maker, we are safe! When we reached that dreadful pit of Carkoon, Artoo threw a lightsaber to Master Luke – he had been hiding it all along! Together with Lando, Chewbacca, Captain Solo and Princess Leia, Master Luke defeated the evil Hutt and destroyed the Sail Barge!

ENTRY: 7

The Emperor is building another Death Star. The Rebel Alliance has to destroy it before it's too late. The generator that powers the Death Star's energy shield is on the forest moon of Endor. If we can deactivate it, our fighters can blast the Death Star. Lando will lead the fighter attack against the Death Star, while Captain Solo – now General Solo – takes a strike team to Endor.

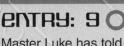

ENTRY: 8

We are on Endor. Something most surprising has happened! A tribe of Ewoks think that I am a god! They are going to help us to reach the shield generator!

ENTRY: 9

Master Luke has told Princess Leia that she is his twin sister and that Darth Vader is their father. But Darth Vader can sense Master Luke's presence, so he must leave us. He is going to surrender to the Imperial troops!

ENTRY: 10

With the help of the Ewoks, we attacked the shield generator. But it was a trap! The Emperor knew what we were doing and we have been captured. We're doomed!

ENTRY: 11

The brave little Ewoks have rescued us! After a tremendous battle, the stormtroopers have been defeated and General Solo and Princess Leia are trying to destroy the shield generator. Artoo did a magnificent job and now we just have to hope that we are in time.

ENTRY: 12

They did it! While Master Luke was facing the Emperor and Darth Vader, General Solo deactivated the shield generator and Lando's team was able to destroy the Death Star! Master Luke's father turned on the Emperor and helped to destroy him. Across the galaxy, everyone is celebrating. The Empire is no more, and the Jedi have returned!

WORDS OF WISDOM

Use the words in the centre to complete these famous quotes. Think carefully before you make your mind up – things are not always as easy as they seem!

1
"_____ leads to jealousy. The shadow of _____ that is."

2
"Oh, *great warrior*, hmm? _____ not make one great."

3
"No...try not. Do or do not. There is no _____."

4
"Size matters not. Look at me. Judge me by my _____ do you?"

5
"Train yourself to let go of everything you fear to _____."

ATTACHMENT
DARK SIDE
DARTH VADER
FEAR
FORCE
GREED
LEARN
LIFE
LOSE
LOSS
SIZE
SUFFERING
TRY
WARS

6
"I sense much _____ in you."

7
"May the _____ be with you."

8
"Much to _____ you still have."

9
"Death is a natural part of _____."

10
"Fear leads to anger; anger leads to hate; hate leads to _____."

11
"The boy you trained – gone, he is; consumed by _____."

12
"The fear of _____ is a path to the _____."

JEDI DICTIONARY OF TERMS

COUNCIL CHAMBER

LIGHTSABER

MASTER

ARCHIVES
The area of the Jedi Temple on Coruscant that contains the history of the Jedi.

CONCORDANCE OF FEALTY
An ancient Jedi tradition in which two Jedi trade lightsabers for a short time in order to prove that they trust one another completely.

CONTEMPLATION STATION
A spacious and graceful place for calm contemplation and reflection, located around the Jedi High Council holomap room.

COUNCIL CHAMBER
A place of open thought and speech, a realm of mutual respect and a haven of shared noble purpose. The 12 members sit in a ring of chairs that are spaced equally around the chamber.

DARK JEDI
Any Jedi who uses the Force for evil ends. Most Dark Jedi begin as naïve and idealistic Jedi Knights, but they are corrupted by their lust for power, the lure of forbidden knowledge and their uncontrollable rage.

FIELD KIT
A collection of useful items carried by a Jedi during most missions. A typical Jedi field kit contains an underwater breathing device, a comlink, multitools, the Jedi's lightsaber, a compact holoprojector, several food and energy capsules, and medical supplies.

FORCE PUSH
A skill that allows a Jedi to change the distribution and nature of the Force to move objects.

FORCE REFRESH
An intimate sharing of the Force between two Jedi. This rejuvenates and renews them.

GATHERING
The term for the formal meetings between the members of the Jedi Council.

GREAT LIBRARY OF OSSUS
A giant archive of Jedi knowledge, books, artefacts and Holocrons located on the quiet planet of Ossus.

HIGH COUNCIL
The governors of Jedi affairs. The Jedi High Council is composed of 12 members.

HOLOCRON
A palm-sized glowing cube of crystal that uses old-fashioned hologramic technology to provide an interactive learning tool. A holocron can only be activated by a Jedi.

HOLOMAP ROOM
A pyramid system of holomaps that allows 12 teams to monitor Jedi activities throughout the galaxy. Potential problems are transferred to larger-scale holomaps for the attention of more senior Jedi.

JEDI
The noble warriors who study the Force and use their powers to protect the galaxy from evil. The trained Jedi can tap into and manipulate the Force to do amazing feats.

LIGHTSABER
A blade of pure energy used by Jedi Knights and Sith warriors. Each lightsaber is handcrafted as part of a Jedi's training and may have unique design elements. A lightsaber's energy blade is produced by several crystals connected to a power source inside the lightsaber's handle.

MASTER
The pinnacle of the Jedi order. Becoming a Jedi Master requires patience, inner strength, wisdom and a deep connection to and understanding of the Force.

PADAWAN
A Jedi apprentice, often recognized by a short haircut and a thin plait. Apprentices are raised and trained at the Jedi Temple. If a Padawan decides to leave his training as a Jedi Knight, he must hand his lightsaber over to his Master before leaving.

TEMPLE
Home of the Jedi order on Coruscant. The flat temple is crowned by five towering spires, which house the most important rooms, including the Jedi Council chamber.

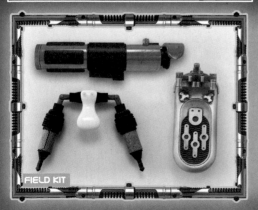
FIELD KIT

ARCHIVES

TEMPLE

A TESTING TIME

You are on the path to becoming a true Jedi Knight. But beware anger, fear and aggression...the dark side are they. Once you start down the dark path, forever will it dominate your destiny. Sense the Force around you and remember that a Jedi's strength flows from the Force.

1. After a mighty duel, your evil opponent is at your mercy. What do you do?
a. End your opponent's life. They would do the same to you!
b. Take your opponent captive and return to the Jedi Council.
c. Wait for reinforcements to arrive.

2. You have spent a long time handcrafting your own lightsaber as part of your training. What does it look like?
a. It looks exactly like your Master's lightsaber, which you have always admired.
b. It is simple, but you designed it yourself and no one else will have one the same.
c. It is unique and unusual – it makes people stare and opponents cower!

3. Do you believe in destiny?
a. I believe that a true Jedi creates his own destiny.
b. Yes, our destiny is decided even before we are born.
c. There is no such thing as destiny.

Answers: 1. a. 6 b. 10 c. 2 **2.** a. 2 b. 10 c. 6 **3.** a. 10 b. 6 c. 2

24-30 – You have a deep understanding of the Jedi way and are deeply attuned to the Force. The Jedi Order will be fortunate to have you as a Knight.

12-22 – The Force is strong with you, but you are at a dangerous point in your journey to become a Jedi Knight. You are tempted by the seductive power of the dark side. Train yourself to think about the consequences of your actions.

6-10 – The patient, calm mind of a Jedi you do not possess. Turn your thoughts away from becoming a Jedi Knight, for now; perhaps you will learn more.

PAGE 21 WORDSEARCH

B	Q	E	P	O	E	M	P	A	T	H	Y	R	V	G	D	L	F	P
A	X	M	D	U	F	L	S	G	O	R	T	J	I	L	N	P	E	C
S	E	K	L	P	J	X	W	I	D	N	G	K	M	R	H	E	L	Y
W	Y	T	S	E	N	O	H	V	S	B	R	E	C	T	L	A	I	F
H	A	R	P	A	D	U	G	K	L	X	N	C	J	M	E	C	W	S
Y	M	U	L	R	T	K	Q	E	H	A	V	N	I	S	U	E	H	T
O	N	H	T	I	E	M	E	A	O	U	K	E	L	D	W	B	N	Y
C	L	O	U	F	T	S	Y	G	N	I	A	L	R	E	D	L	X	F
O	J	K	G	U	Y	H	R	I	V	D	F	O	H	L	U	S	T	Q
N	S	I	L	X	T	G	U	O	S	K	A	V	E	L	M	H	O	N
T	P	F	M	E	I	J	G	K	N	U	I	E	D	V	A	R	W	L
R	D	V	T	Q	N	F	H	T	K	S	Y	N	O	M	R	A	H	O
O	K	F	B	S	U	U	M	V	H	D	I	E	A	L	W	G	R	S
L	R	M	U	T	M	D	A	T	W	H	U	R	C	A	Q	P	J	S
Y	T	I	P	I	M	F	S	O	X	B	Q	V	I	E	S	F	Y	O
T	F	B	L	P	O	N	I	S	E	R	V	X	W	L	O	D	P	I
E	N	I	X	A	C	U	D	T	M	B	P	H	A	V	I	L	W	K
W	T	P	D	H	A	I	J	E	U	P	M	L	P	T	B	T	S	F
X	L	B	V	V	C	O	M	P	A	S	S	I	O	N	U	E	W	T

PAGE 28 WORDS OF WISDOM

1. Attachment, greed
2. Wars
3. Try
4. Size
5. Lose
6. Fear
7. Force
8. Learn
9. Life
10. Suffering
11. Darth Vader
12. Loss, dark side

BATTLE
THE

A Sith Lord and a Jedi Knight are racing towards the Death Star across the galaxy. The Sith Lord will use it to destroy a planet. The Jedi Knight will destroy the Death Star itself. Which way will your destiny lead you? Will you embrace the unlimited power of the Sith, or will you stay true to the Jedi way? Only one person can gain control of the galaxy!

START

You stop to help a Neimoidian in distress. Miss a go.

You use peaceful negotiations to end a war.

Try to use the Force to read your opponent's mind.

You defeat an evil Sith apprentice. Go forward 1 square.

You drop your lightsaber. Go back 1 square.

Talk like Chewbacca until your next go.

Tell a joke.

Sing the *Star Wars* theme tune.

You are knocked out in battle. Go back 2 squares.

Do an imitation of your favourite Jedi.

You duel and defeat a Sith Lord. Go forward 2 squares.

OF FORCE

You will need: 1 dice, 1 marker per player

How to play:

Roll the dice to decide who will play as the Jedi and who will play as the Sith.

Place your markers on the board.

Decide who will go first and roll the dice again.

Move your marker along the board and follow the instructions where you land.

The first player to reach the Death Star is the winner!

Decide what your Sith name will be.

START

You destroy two Jedi starfighters. Go forward 1 square.

Pull your scariest face.

You capture a rebel. Have another go.

You have nightmares and oversleep. Go back 2 squares

You lose control of your starfighter. Miss a go.

Breathe like Darth Vader until your next go.

Design your own lightsaber in 60 seconds.

The Emperor is angry with you. Go back 1 square.

Do an imitation of Emperor Palpatine.

Your probes locate a rebel base. Go forward 2 squares.

33

Do you have what it takes to be one of the most powerful and legendary beings in the galaxy? A Dark Jedi must be able to use their anger to sense and control the Living Force. Discover your destiny – if you dare!

1. What do you value most highly?
a. Your friends and childhood memories.
b. The respect and admiration of those around you.
c. Your connection to the Force.

2. What do you fear most?
a. The loss of things or people you care about.
b. The breakdown of society as you know it.
c. Sensing what the future holds.

3. Your Master tells you to do something that you don't agree with. What do you do?
a. Find a quiet and peaceful place where you can meditate on your best course of action.
b. You do not question your Master – he is wiser that you and learning means obedience.
c. Rush to tell the Jedi Council all about it.

Answers: 1. a. 6 b. 10 c. 2 **2.** a. 10 b. 6 c. 2 **3.** a. 6 b. 10 c. 2

24-30 – You have released your anger and allowed it to guide you towards power and glory. The Emperor will find many uses for you!

12-22 – Life as a Dark Jedi appeals to you, but you must show more commitment to the way of the Sith before you can truly turn to the dark side.

6-10 – You have all the makings of a treacherous and misguided Jedi. You will never be a great Sith Lord!

35

ANSWERS

PAGE 47 WAR OF WORDS

H	A	R	D	E	S	I	R	E	P	Y	H	I	Y	V	E	Q	A	M
S	F	P	V	Q	N	K	A	U	L	N	P	R	V	Y	K	N	U	H
D	K	H	P	F	L	E	J	E	H	O	L	F	N	W	G	T	L	A
S	E	N	O	H	V	S	E	V	Q	I	X	S	E	T	B	I	T	N
H	U	U	M	X	T	S	I	A	G	S	G	F	P	L	X	Q	S	G
F	P	E	T	N	O	L	D	W	A	S	H	X	Q	R	U	H	L	E
V	C	D	A	C	P	U	F	S	O	E	T	I	B	H	S	F	C	R
I	X	P	H	L	U	H	M	Q	K	R	B	J	F	E	A	T	N	O
M	K	S	G	I	Q	A	H	D	U	G	M	A	F	K	T	N	W	V
A	T	B	H	F	J	U	S	T	L	G	N	I	X	A	C	U	D	T
K	G	U	Y	H	P	I	S	J	C	A	G	H	O	V	A	S	F	K
J	W	F	I	M	T	B	J	X	O	X	U	A	H	W	B	E	L	S
N	I	A	L	R	E	D	L	X	F	I	N	T	F	M	A	R	U	W
B	E	U	T	W	F	A	C	K	I	Q	S	R	L	R	V	H	D	B
S	S	E	N	H	S	I	F	L	E	S	V	E	E	F	J	B	T	E
G	U	O	S	K	A	V	E	L	M	H	O	D	C	H	K	U	F	P
U	E	H	T	M	D	A	T	W	H	U	B	C	A	Q	T	P	F	M
G	R	E	E	D	A	M	S	I	B	W	A	U	C	E	D	I	R	P
A	T	H	Y	R	V	G	D	L	F	P	H	V	S	B	R	E	C	M

PAGE 45 CROSSWORD

Across
1. Mos Eisley
3. Tatooine
7. Endor
8. Gungan
12. Utapau
13. Dagobah
15. lightsaber
17. Geonosis
18. Naboo

Down
1. *Millennium Falcon*
2. Luke
3. Tusken Raiders
4. Obi-Wan Kenobi
5. Ewoks
6. Darth Maul
9. Darth Vader
10. Jango Fett
11. Protocol
14. Han Solo
16. Ice

Use this chart to study the development of the galactic legends, and see how the dark side is the path to power.

LEIA SKYWALKER

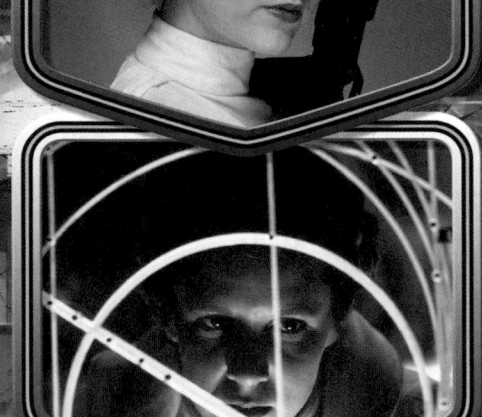

Idealistic and determined, Leia has her mother's beauty and sense of justice. She is willing to risk her life to destroy the Empire.

OBI-WAN KENOBI

Obi-Wan remained true to his foolish Jedi beliefs all his life. He watched over Luke and tried to teach him the same Jedi lies he once taught Luke's father.

EMPEROR PALPATINE

Cunning, intelligent and ambitious, Palpatine spent years unravelling the corrupt Republic, until at last ultimate power was his. He formed the Empire and ruled without mercy.

HEROES AND VILLAINS

ANAKIN SKYWALKER

Once an idealistic young Jedi, Anakin Skywalker turned to the dark side and became apprentice to the great Sith Lord, Palpatine. As Darth Vader, he is known and feared throughout the galaxy.

PADMÉ AMIDALA

A principled and beautiful Senator, Padmé fell in love with a Jedi and tried to stop his journey to the dark side. She was doomed to failure.

LUKE SKYWALKER

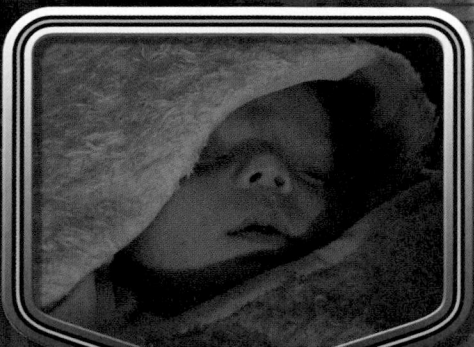

The Force was strong with young Skywalker from the moment he was born. It is his destiny to confront the Emperor and his father, and, possibly, to turn to the dark side, too.

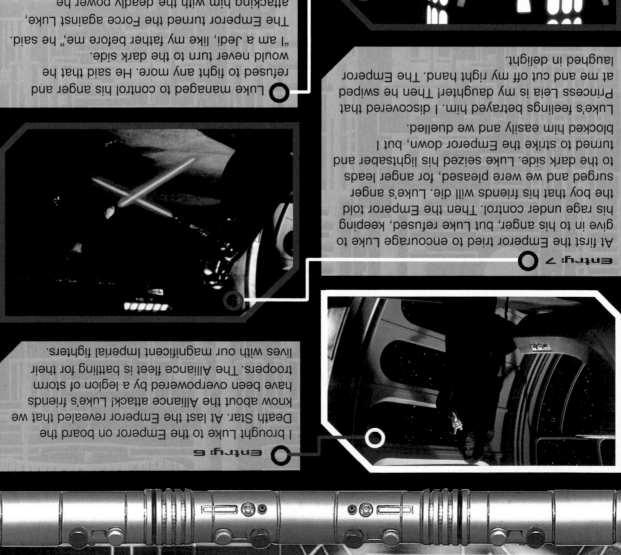

Entry: 6

I brought Luke to the Emperor on board the Death Star. At last the Emperor revealed that we know about the Alliance attack! Luke's friends have been overpowered by a legion of storm troopers. The Alliance fleet is battling for their lives with our magnificent Imperial fighters.

Entry: 7

At first the Emperor tried to encourage Luke to give in to his anger, but Luke refused, keeping his rage under control. Then the Emperor told the boy that his friends will die. Luke's anger surged and we were pleased, for anger leads to the dark side. Luke seized his lightsaber and turned to strike the Emperor down, but I blocked him easily and we duelled.

Luke's feelings betrayed him. I discovered that Princess Leia is my daughter! Then he swiped at me and cut off my right hand. The Emperor laughed in delight.

Luke managed to control his anger and refused to fight any more. He said that he would never turn to the dark side.
"I am a Jedi, like my father before me," he said. The Emperor turned the Force against Luke, attacking him with the deadly power he commands. I watched my son twisting in agony on the floor, begging for help. Deep within me, I felt the old Anakin awake again. I thought of the old times, of Obi-Wan and of Padmé. Then I knew what I had to do!

I picked up the Emperor and hurled him down the power shaft. He died in an explosion of blue Force lightning, but it hit me, too, and I knew that I was dying.
The Rebels have won and the Empire is destroyed. I asked Luke to remove my mask. He saw my face, hideous and deformed. My life too has been twisted and evil because of my arrogance and greed. But at least the horror has ended.

Entry: 8

At last I have become one with the Force. I have been reunited with Yoda and Obi-Wan Kenobi.
The dark times are at an end.

Year: 4

Entry: 1

In secret, the Galactic Empire has begun construction on a new Death Star. When completed, this ultimate weapon will spell certain doom for the Rebels. I have come to tell the Commander that the Emperor himself is coming to oversee the creation.

Entry: 2

The Emperor's ship has landed on the Death Star. He has ordered me to bring young Luke Skywalker to him. The boy has grown stronger since I fought him, and only together can we now turn him to the dark side.

Entry: 3

We know that the Alliance Rebels want to destroy the Death Star. To have any chance, they must deactivate its energy shield, which is powered from the forest moon of Endor. When they have deactivated the shield, their fighters can attack the Death Star. This is how we will trap them!

Entry: 4

I have come to Endor and I can sense that Luke is here. The Emperor foresaw that Luke would seek me out.

Entry: 5

Luke has surrendered to the Imperial troops and has been brought to me. He said that I have forgotten my true self and that deep down I am still Anakin Skywalker! I feel unexpected conflict within. Luke has urged me to let go of my hate. But I must obey my Master.

ENTRY: 5 ○

Our sensors detected the *Millennium Falcon* as it left the asteroid field. We fired on it, but suddenly it disappeared from our radar. It must have gone into light speed.

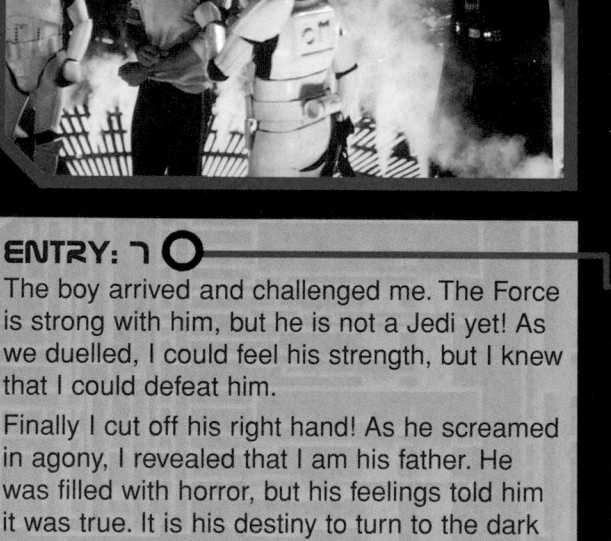

○ ENTRY: 6

At last I have captured Princess Leia, the Wookie Chewbacca and Han Solo. Boba Fett followed the *Millennium Falcon* to Lando Calrissian's mining colony. I forced Lando to betray them to save his people. I have tortured Chewbacca and Han Solo, and thrown them into a cell. I know that Luke will come to rescue his friends.

When Luke arrives I will put him in a carbon freezing facility and take him to the Emperor, but first I must test it. I will freeze Solo and give him to Boba Fett. He can collect the reward from Jabba the Hutt.

ENTRY: 7 ○

The boy arrived and challenged me. The Force is strong with him, but he is not a Jedi yet! As we duelled, I could feel his strength, but I knew that I could defeat him.

Finally I cut off his right hand! As he screamed in agony, I revealed that I am his father. He was filled with horror, but his feelings told him it was true. It is his destiny to turn to the dark side. I asked him to help me destroy the Emperor, so we can rule the galaxy together as father and son! But the foolish boy would rather die. He rolled over the edge of the platform and dropped into the abyss.

○ ENTRY: 8

Lando Calrissian has let the prisoners go, and they have rescued Luke. I sensed too late that he is still alive. But he must turn to the dark side – or die.

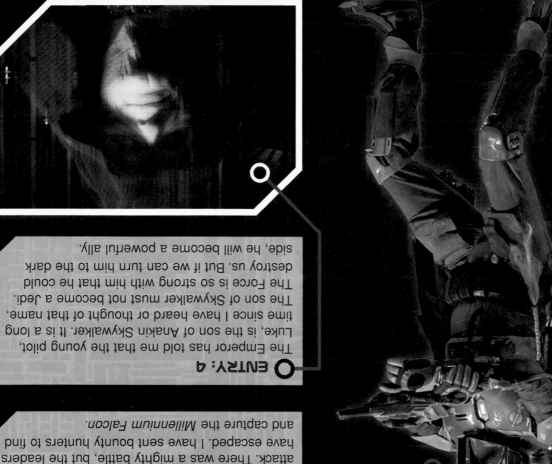

YEAR: 3

ENTRY: 1

The end is coming for the rebellion. Our Imperial troops have driven the rebel forces from their hidden base and pursued them across the galaxy. I am determined to find the young pilot who had such a strong link to the Force. I have dispatched thousands of remote probes into the far reaches of space.

ENTRY: 2

At last one of my probes has found the rebel base. It is on the remote ice world of Hoth. I will go there and destroy them once and for all.

ENTRY: 3

We arrived before the Rebels had evacuated and I sent troops down to the planet for a surface attack. There was a mighty battle, but the leaders have escaped. I have sent bounty hunters to find and capture the Millennium Falcon.

ENTRY: 4

The Emperor has told me that the young pilot, Luke, is the son of Anakin Skywalker. It is a long time since I have heard or thought of that name. The son of Skywalker must not become a Jedi. The Force is so strong with him that he could destroy us. But if we can turn him to the dark side, he will become a powerful ally.

ENTRY: 9

It hardly seems possible, but the Rebels have destroyed the Death Star. It is a blow for the Empire, but we can still defeat the Rebels.

The boy who sent his torpedoes into the weak spot is a skilled pilot. The Force is strong with him. I wonder who he is...

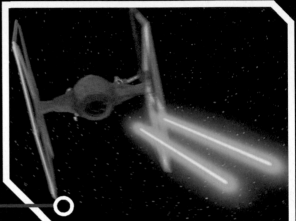

ENTRY: 8

We have discovered the rebel base on Yavin 4. Now we will destroy the traitors. I will pilot my own fighter. There is still no pilot better than me!

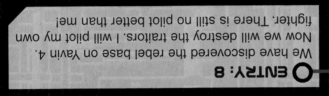

ENTRY: 7

I came face to face with Obi-Wan and we ignited our lightsabers. This time, I was the Master! At last I struck him down, but his body vanished!

While I was defeating Obi-Wan, the Rebels rescued the Princess. I have allowed them to escape, but the Death Star is following them. They will lead us to the headquarters of the rebellion.

Before he died, Obi-Wan said that if I struck him down he would become more powerful than I could imagine. What did he mean?

ENTRY: 6

When the ship landed on the Death Star, I sensed a presence I haven't felt for many long years. It was my old Master, Obi-Wan. I will defeat him at last!

YEAR: 0

○ **ENTRY: 1**

The treacherous rebel spaceships, striking from a hidden base, have won a victory against us. They have stolen the plans of the Death Star. I know that Princess Leia has the plans, and I will catch her long before she reaches safety.

○ **ENTRY: 2**

Princess Leia is my prisoner, but the plans are not with her. She must have given them to someone before she was caught. Some droids were sent down to Tatooine, and I have sent troops after them.

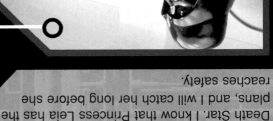

○ **ENTRY: 3**

I have tortured the stubborn Princess Leia but she will not reveal the location of the Rebels' secret base. I have set a course for her home planet of Alderaan. My storm troopers have discovered the droids. They have been joined by some humans and have a ship, the *Millennium Falcon*, but my troops were unable to stop them.

○ **ENTRY: 4**

Grand Moff Tarkin and I told Princess Leia to reveal the location of the rebel base or we would destroy her home planet. At last she gave us the name. Of course we destroyed Alderaan anyway. Only when all our enemies are dead can we have peace.

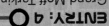

○ **ENTRY: 5**

Leia has lied about the location of the rebel base! She is awaiting execution in the detention cells. As we held position beside the remains of Alderaan, the *Millennium Falcon* appeared close by. They must have the stolen plans! I have captured them with a tractor beam.

CROSSWORD

How well do you know the legends of *Star Wars*?

Across

1. Where did Obi-Wan Kenobi meet Han Solo? (3,6)
3. On which planet did Anakin Skywalker first meet Obi-Wan Kenobi? (8)
7. The Death Star's energy shield was powered from which forest moon? (5)
8. What species is Jar Jar Binks? (6)
12. Where did Obi-Wan Kenobi defeat General Grievous? (6)
13. Where did Luke go to find Master Yoda? (7)
15. What is the name of the Jedi weapon? (10)
17. Where did the first battle of the Clone Wars take place? (8)
18. What was Padmé Amidala's home planet? (5)

Down

1. What was the name of Han Solo's ship? (10,6)
2. Who is the 'son of Skywalker'? (4)
3. Who kidnapped Anakin's mother? (6,7)
4. Who fought Darth Vader on the planet of Mustafar? (3-3,6)
5. Which species helped the Rebel Alliance destroy the Death Star's energy shield? (5)
6. Who was Darth Sidious's first apprentice? (5,4)
9. Who killed Emperor Palpatine? (5,5)
10. Who was the clone army cloned from? (5,4)
11. What kind of droid is C-3PO? (8)
14. Who was frozen in carbonite and delivered to Jabba the Hutt? (3,4)
16. What covers the Planet Hoth? (3)

BOUNTY HUNTERS

The bounty hunters are a necessary tool for controlling the Empire. For the right money, they will go anywhere and kill anyone. The Empire often uses them to hunt down rebels.

Jango Fett

Resourceful and dangerous, Jango Fett was known throughout the criminal underworld as the best bounty hunter in the galaxy. A sleek armoured suit hid his rugged face and strangely tattooed forearms. Fett was armed with retractable wrist blades, dual pistols, a snare and other concealed weaponry. His harnessed backpack, capable of jet propulsion and missile projection, gave him an advantage over his opponents.

Fett was the original for the clone army and was hardened by a life of dangerous work and ruthless operations. He died during the Battle of Geonosis, when Mace Windu beheaded him.

Zam Wesell

Zam Wesell was a dangerous, heavily armed bounty hunter hired by Jango Fett to eliminate Senator Amidala. Swift and deadly, Wesell was an excellent assassin and tracker. However, she got more than she bargained for when her assassination attempt was foiled by the Senator's Jedi protectors, who pursued her on a harrowing chase through Coruscant. She was killed by Jango Fett before she could give the Jedi his name.

Boba Fett

Boba Fett is a pure genetic replication of Jango Fett. He was born in the cloning facilities of Kamino. Unlike the other clones, his genetic structure was not altered, accelerated or weakened. When Mace Windu killed his 'father', he was turned against the Jedi order forever.

He grew up to become the most notorious bounty hunter in the galaxy, scouring the stars for profit and personal reward. Frequently employed by the crime lord Jabba the Hutt, Boba Fett has also been commissioned by Darth Vader.

Greedo

Greedo was a Rodian bounty hunter who made the mistake of challenging Han Solo. At blaster point, he demanded that Solo pay his debt to Jabba. When Solo claimed he didn't have the money with him, Greedo lost his patience and opened fire. His shot missed – but Solo's did not.

Greedo was survived by a relative named Beedo, who took his place in Jabba the Hutt's court.

WAR OF WORDS

Use the Force to look for these words in the panel below. They are all words that are important to a Sith Lord. Gain one point for each word you find. The words may be upside down, diagonal or back to front.

Desire	Fear
Greed	Envy
Anger	Aggression
Hatred	Pride
Jealousy	Selfishness

TOP SECRET!

Knowledge is power! How many of these facts did you already know?

The exploits of Skywalker and Kenobi became legendary throughout the Republic. Anakin was known as the 'Hero With No Fear' for his daring heroics. Obi-Wan's tactics earned him the title of 'the Negotiator.' Many times, he was able to cease hostilities without the raising of a single blaster.

Darth Bane was a Sith Lord who lived approximately one thousand years before Anakin Skywalker. It was he who ensured that the Sith survived in secrecy only as one Master and one apprentice at a time.

Jedi Master Mace Windu once destroyed an entire army of battle droids bare handed.

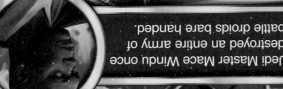

Leia Organa was the youngest Senator ever in the Imperial Senate, representing Alderaan.

A stormtrooper's suit contains a utility belt, which has a comlink, a grappling hook, handcuff binders and macrobinoculars.

Luke Skywalker honed his piloting skills alongside Biggs Darklighter in Tatooine's Beggar's Canyon, racing his T-16 Skyhopper.

Padmé Amidala volunteered in the Refugee Relief Movement as a youth. At the age of eight, she joined the Apprentice Legislature and became an Apprentice Legislator at age 11. By the age of 14, she was Queen of Naboo.

Darth Maul became a Sith when Darth Sidious sent him to a planet in the Outer Rim. For nearly a month, Maul was attacked by assassin droids in desert, swamp and mountain terrains. The final part of the confrontation was to battle Sidious himself. After the training, Sidious and Maul went to the Sith archives, where they found the designs for Darth Maul's double-bladed lightsaber.

A rogue Jedi Knight founded the Sith when he realised that the real power of the Force lay not in the light, but in the dark. Failing to gain approval for his beliefs from the Council, he broke with the order and departed with his knowledge and his skills, swearing that he could bring down those who had dismissed him.

YEAR: -19

ENTRY: 1

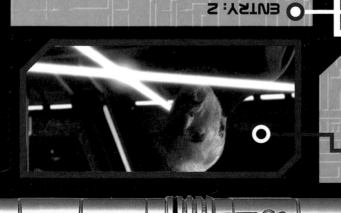

The Clone Wars are still raging across the galaxy. The droid leader, General Grievous, kidnapped Chancellor Palpatine. Obi-Wan and I rescued Palpatine and I killed Count Dooku, but General Grievous has escaped.

ENTRY: 2

I have seen Padmé for the first time in months. She has wonderful news! I am going to be a father! This is the happiest day of my life!

ENTRY: 3

Last night, I had dreams of Padmé dying in childbirth. It was like the dreams I had about my mother before she died. Padmé thinks we should speak to Obi-Wan, but I don't want him to know anything.

ENTRY: 4

I have spoken to Yoda about my dreams, but he just said that the fear of loss is a path to the dark side. I won't let these visions come true!

ENTRY: 5

I am furious! Palpatine appointed me as his representative on the Jedi Council, but they have refused to give me the title of 'Master'. It is outrageous! I'm more powerful than any of them! After the meeting, Obi-Wan asked me to report on all of the Chancellor's dealings – to spy on my good friend and mentor!

ENTRY: 6

Palpatine told me about Darth Plagueis, a Sith Lord who could keep the ones he loved from dying. He said that it is possible to learn this skill, but not from a Jedi. Perhaps I can save Padmé!

ENTRY: 7

General Grievous is on the planet Utapau. Obi-Wan has gone to face him. That mission should be mine! I'm one of the most powerful Jedi, but they don't trust me.

ENTRY: 8

Palpatine is a Sith Lord! He has offered to teach me the ways of the dark side, which can save Padmé's life. He said that my anger focuses me and makes me strong. What he said made sense, but I knew I had to turn him over to the Jedi Council.

ENTRY: 9

Mace has gone to arrest Palpatine. If the Chancellor dies in the fight, I will lose all chance of saving Padmé! I have to stop Mace!

ENTRY: 10

I arrived just in time. I could not let Palpatine die – nothing is more important than saving Padmé! Mace had to die.

Palpatine asked me to fulfil my destiny and become his apprentice. I have agreed. I can't live without Padmé. I kneeled and pledged myself to the ways of the Sith. Everything the Jedi taught me has been lies. Henceforth I shall be known as Darth Vader.

ENTRY: 11

I have destroyed the younglings in the Temple. The Jedi are traitors and must die. My loyalties lie with the Chancellor and with the Senate...and with Padmé.

ENTRY: 12

I have come to Mustafar to cut the Separatist leaders down. I can feel my anger filling me and making me strong! But Padmé's ship has landed nearby. What is she doing here?

ENTRY: 13

Padmé brought Obi-Wan to kill me! Enraged, I used my Force strength to choke her, but Obi-Wan stopped me and we duelled. Obi-Wan tried to make me listen to his Jedi lies, but I know better now. Obi-Wan cut off my legs and arm. As I lay in agony, molten lava set my clothes alight and I began to burn! I hate Obi-Wan!

I am now in the Imperial Rehabilitation Centre. My Master has saved my life, but Padmé and our unborn child are dead. I will never allow feelings of love to control me again. I am Darth Vader, and the galaxy will tremble at my name!

YEAR: -22

ENTRY: 1

It is ten years since I last saw Padmé, but I am going to meet her again at last! The Separatist movement, under the leadership of Count Dooku, wants to leave the Republic. Padmé, who is now a Senator, is coming to the Galactic Senate to vote against creating an Army of the Republic.

ENTRY: 2

Someone is trying to kill Padmé. She has been placed under the protection of Master Obi-Wan Kenobi and me. After ten years, she is more beautiful than ever, but she still thinks of me as a little boy.

ENTRY: 3

It seems that a bounty hunter is behind the attacks on Padmé. Obi-Wan is going to track him down. It is my job to escort Padmé back to Naboo and protect her. Obi-Wan does not think I am ready for this assignment, but he never appreciates my skills!

ENTRY: 4

As we travelled in disguise to Naboo, I told Padmé about being a Jedi and how Obi-Wan is holding me back. I think Padmé has begun to see that I am no longer a child.

ENTRY: 5

We are safe on Naboo, and Padmé and I have grown very close. I want to tell her that I am in love with her, but a Jedi is not allowed to love.

ENTRY: 6

I told Padmé how I feel, but she said that our love can never be. I know that she is right. It would destroy us.

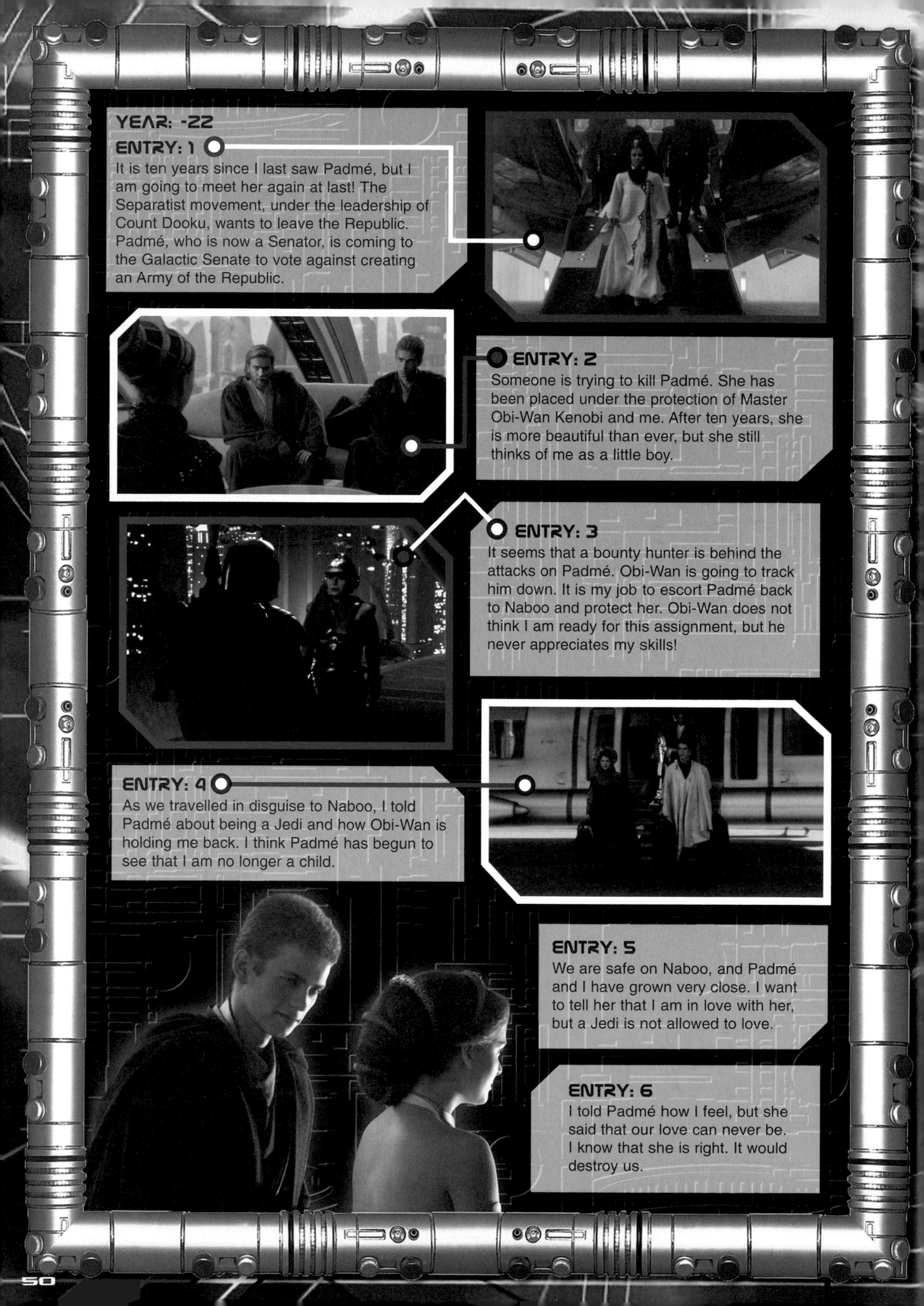

ENTRY: 7

Last night I had a terrible nightmare. I think that my mother is in danger! Padmé and I are going to Tatooine, even though I will be disobeying the Jedi Council's orders.

ENTRY: 8

We have arrived on Tatooine. My mother has been captured by Tusken Raiders. I must find her!

ENTRY: 9

I found my mother at the Tusken Raiders camp, but I was too late. She died in my arms. A great rage filled me and I slaughtered the Tusken Raiders – men, women and children. I will never fail again. I will become the most powerful Jedi ever.

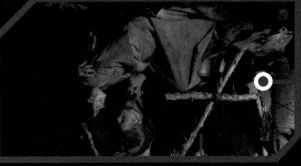

ENTRY: 10

Obi-Wan has found a huge clone army that has been created for the Republic. He also found Jango Fett, the bounty hunter who tried to kill Padmé. He has followed Jango to Geonosis, but now he is in danger. The Jedi Council doesn't want me to go and help Obi-Wan, but I will not listen to them!

ENTRY: 11

When Padmé and I arrived on Geonosis we were captured and condemned to death with Obi-Wan. Padmé told me that she loves me! Just in time, a company of Jedi arrived and an almighty battle began.

Obi-Wan and I fought Count Dooku, but he defeated Obi-Wan and chopped my arm off! I fell to the ground next to my Master. Then Master Yoda challenged Dooku. They duelled at lightning speed, but Count Dooku managed to escape.

ENTRY: 12

I have a new mechanical arm – and a new secret. I have married Padmé. I do not know what will happen if the Jedi Council finds out, but she is more important than anything.

Supreme Chancellor Palpatine has given orders for thousands of clone troopers and has sworn to defeat the Separatists. A great war is beginning!

EXCERPTS FROM DARTH VADER'S DIARY

YEAR: -32

ENTRY: 1

It has always been a boring life being Watto's slave here on Tatooine, until today! A Jedi Knight called Qui-Gon Jinn and a girl called Padmé have come looking for parts to repair their ship. Watto has the parts they need, but they have no money.

Padmé is very beautiful. She looks like an angel! I have offered to help Qui-Gon by entering the next podrace and using the prize money to buy parts.

ENTRY: 2

Qui-Gon believes that there is something special about me. He has made a deal with Watto. If I win the podrace, I will be set free! But Watto will not let my mother go, too.

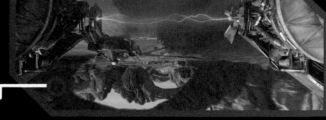

ENTRY: 3

The podrace was so exciting! Crowds of people came to the arena to see the podrace. That cheating Sebulba tried to knock me out of the race, but I got into first place on the final lap and I won. I am free!

ENTRY: 4

I am keen to train as a Jedi, but it was very hard to leave my mother behind. One day I will come back and free her!

Qui-Gon introduced me to his Padawan, Obi-Wan Kenobi. Before we left, we were attacked by a tattooed warrior! We escaped and went to Coruscant.

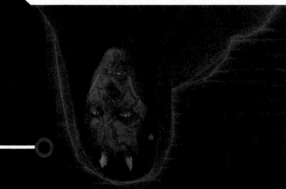

ENTRY: 5

Padmé comes from a planet called Naboo, but it is under attack from the Trade Federation. The Queen is going to ask the Senate for help.

ENTRY: 6

The Jedi Council tested me today. I don't think they were very pleased with me. But Qui-Gon says he will train me himself. I hope that I can be a Jedi like Qui-Gon one day!

ENTRY: 7 O

I have come to Naboo with Padmé, Qui-Gon and Obi-Wan. We went to see the Gungan leader, Boss Nass. Suddenly Padmé said that she is the Queen! She has been using a decoy to fool her enemies. Boss Nass has agreed to help fight the Trade Federation.

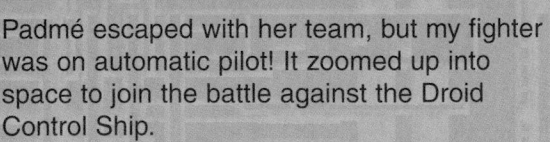

O ENTRY: 8:

I crept into the city with Padmé, Obi-Wan and Qui-Gon. We burst into the landing area and Qui-Gon told me to hide. I climbed into a spare fighter with a droid called R2-D2.

Suddenly droidekas rolled into the hangar and started firing! The tattooed warrior appeared and attacked Qui-Gon and Obi-Wan. I had to do something. I turned the fighter on the droidekas and shot them down.

Padmé escaped with her team, but my fighter was on automatic pilot! It zoomed up into space to join the battle against the Droid Control Ship.

R2-D2 managed to get the fighter out of autopilot and we flew into the Droid Control Ship. I shot at the main reactor and the Droid Control Ship started to lose power. It was time to get out of there! I escaped just as it exploded into tiny pieces.

When I landed back on Naboo, I found that we had won! But the tattoed warrior was a Sith Lord, and he has killed my friend Qui-Gon. O

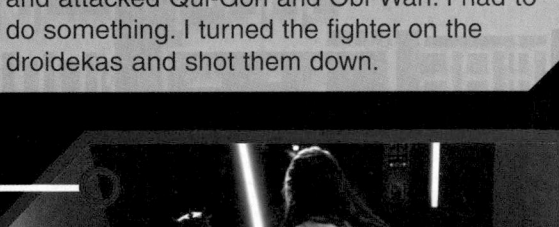

ENTRY: 9 O

We are back on Coruscant. A Senator called Palpatine has been made Supreme Chancellor. Obi-Wan is now a Jedi Knight and I am going to be his Padawan Learner! I will try to be the very best Jedi ever!

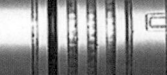

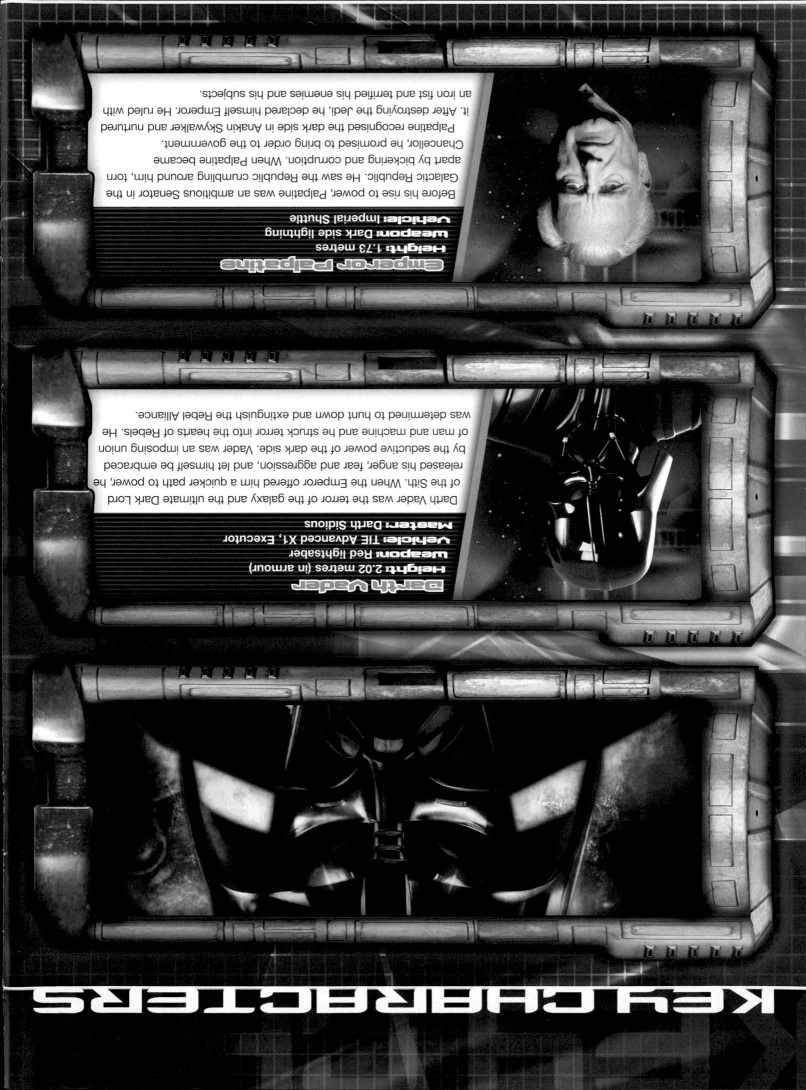

Emperor Palpatine

Height: 1.73 metres
weapon: Dark side lightning
Vehicle: Imperial Shuttle

Before his rise to power, Palpatine was an ambitious Senator in the Galactic Republic. He saw the Republic crumbling around him, torn apart by bickering and corruption. When Palpatine became Chancellor, he promised to bring order to the government. Palpatine recognised the dark side in Anakin Skywalker and nurtured it. After destroying the Jedi, he declared himself Emperor. He ruled with an iron fist and terrified his enemies and his subjects.

Darth Vader

Height: 2.02 metres (in armour)
weapon: Red lightsaber
Vehicle: TIE Advanced X1, Executor
Master: Darth Sidious

Darth Vader was the terror of the galaxy and the ultimate Dark Lord of the Sith. When the Emperor offered him a quicker path to power, he released his anger, fear and aggression, and let himself be embraced by the seductive power of the dark side. Vader was an imposing union of man and machine and he struck terror into the hearts of Rebels. He was determined to hunt down and extinguish the Rebel Alliance.

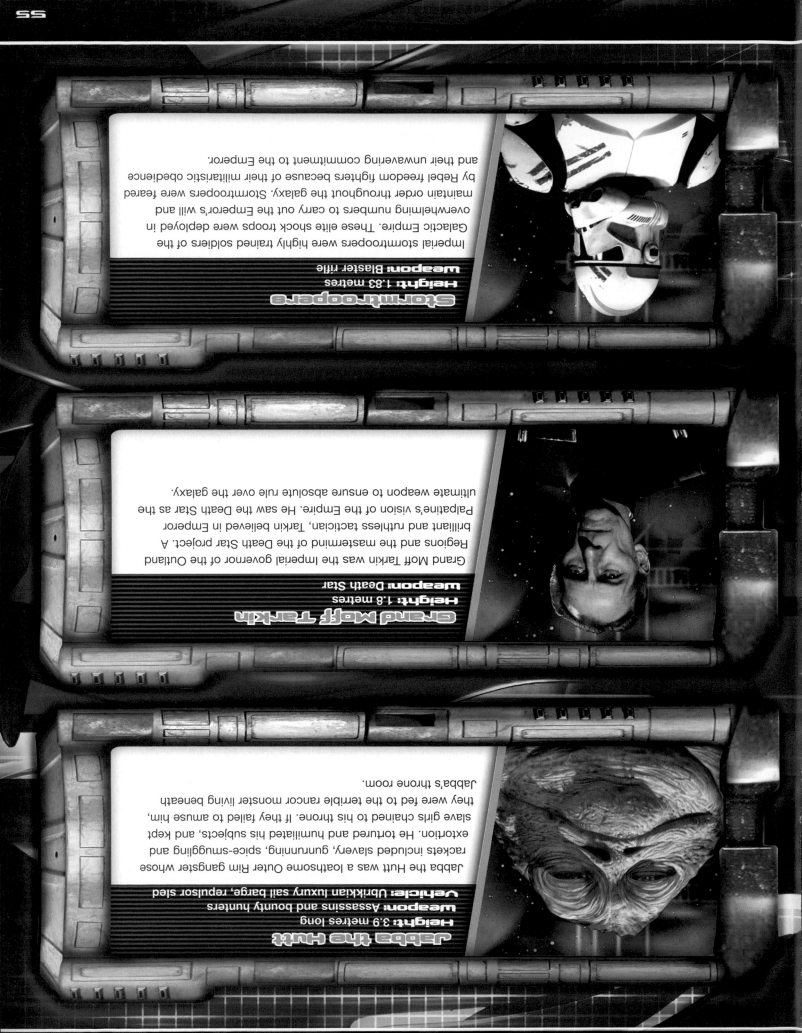

Stormtroopers

Height: 1.83 metres
weapon: Blaster rifle

Imperial stormtroopers were highly trained soldiers of the Galactic Empire. These elite shock troops were deployed in overwhelming numbers to carry out the Emperor's will and maintain order throughout the galaxy. Stormtroopers were feared by Rebel freedom fighters because of their militaristic obedience and their unwavering commitment to the Emperor.

Grand Moff Tarkin

Height: 1.8 metres
weapon: Death Star

Grand Moff Tarkin was the Imperial governor of the Outland Regions and the mastermind of the Death Star project. A brilliant and ruthless tactician, Tarkin believed in Emperor Palpatine's vision of the Empire. He saw the Death Star as the ultimate weapon to ensure absolute rule over the galaxy.

Jabba the Hutt

Height: 3.9 metres long
weapon: Assassins and bounty hunters
vehicle: Ubrikkian luxury sail barge, repulsor sled

Jabba the Hutt was a loathsome Outer Rim gangster whose rackets included slavery, gunrunning, spice-smuggling and extortion. He tortured and humiliated his subjects, and kept slave girls chained to his throne. If they failed to amuse him, they were fed to the terrible rancor monster living beneath Jabba's throne room.

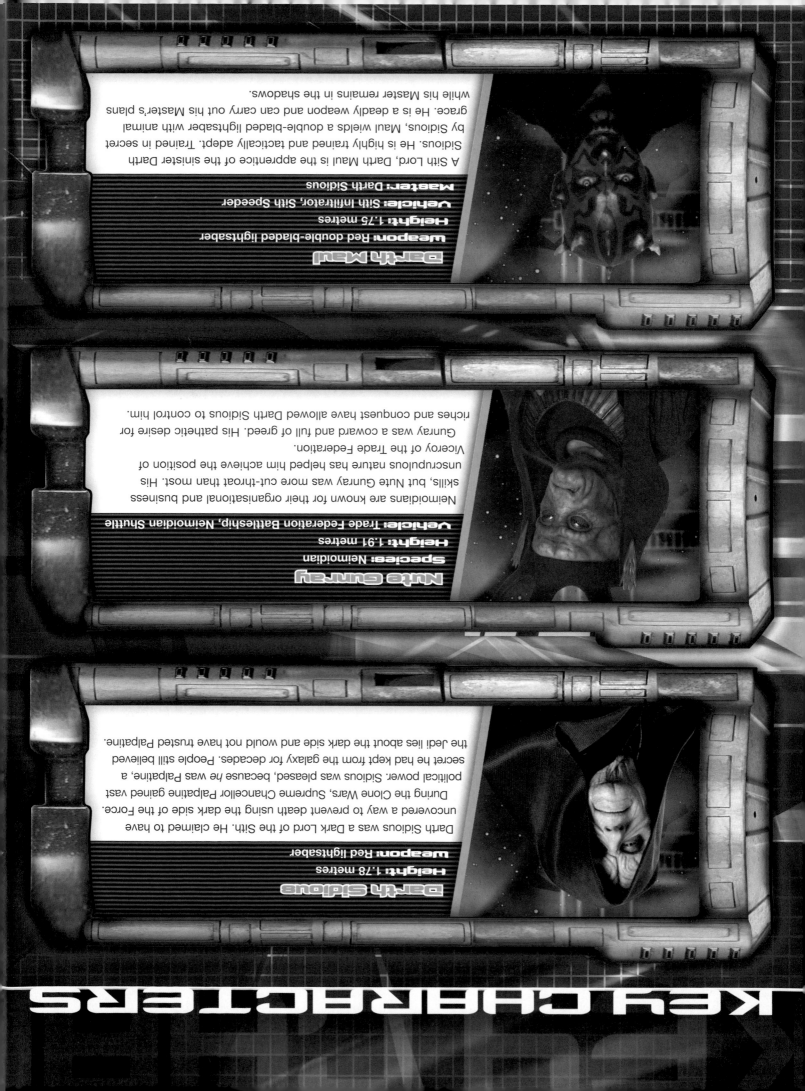

Darth Maul

Weapon: Red double-bladed lightsaber
Height: 1.75 metres
Vehicle: Sith Infiltrator, Sith Speeder
Master: Darth Sidious

A Sith Lord, Darth Maul is the apprentice of the sinister Darth Sidious. He is highly trained and tactically adept. Trained in secret by Sidious, Maul wields a double-bladed lightsaber with animal grace. He is a deadly weapon and can carry out his Master's plans while his Master remains in the shadows.

Nute Gunray

Species: Neimoidian
Height: 1.91 metres
Vehicle: Trade Federation Battleship, Neimoidian Shuttle

Neimoidians are known for their organisational and business skills, but Nute Gunray was more cut-throat than most. His unscrupulous nature has helped him achieve the position of Viceroy of the Trade Federation.
Gunray was a coward and full of greed. His pathetic desire for riches and conquest have allowed Darth Sidious to control him.

Darth Sidious

Height: 1.78 metres
Weapon: Red lightsaber

Darth Sidious was a Dark Lord of the Sith. He claimed to have uncovered a way to prevent death using the dark side of the Force.
During the Clone Wars, Supreme Chancellor Palpatine gained vast political power. Sidious was pleased, because *he* was Palpatine, a secret he had kept from the galaxy for decades. People still believed the Jedi lies about the dark side and would not have trusted Palpatine.

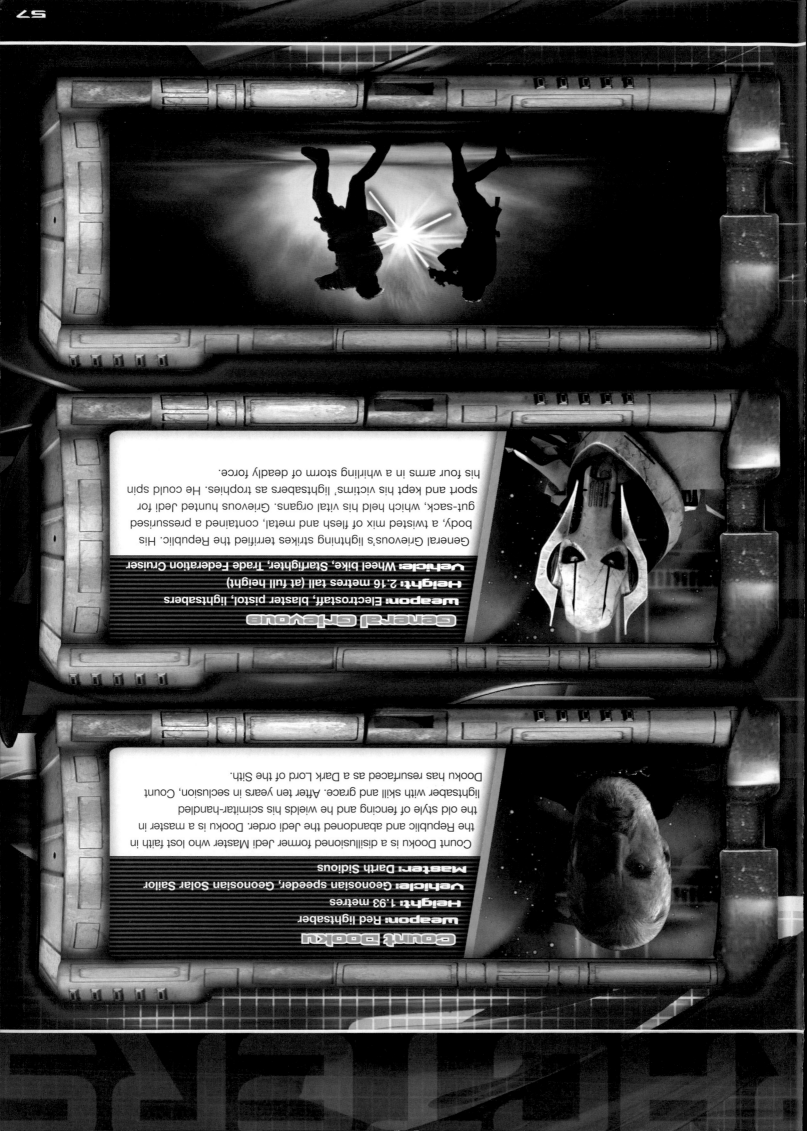

General Grievous

Weapon: Electrostaff, blaster pistol, lightsabers

Height: 2.16 metres tall (at full height)

Vehicle: Wheel bike, Starfighter, Trade Federation Cruiser

General Grievous's lightning strikes terrified the Republic. His body, a twisted mix of flesh and metal, contained a pressurised gut-sack, which held his vital organs. Grievous hunted Jedi for sport and kept his victims' lightsabers as trophies. He could spin his four arms in a whirling storm of deadly force.

Count Dooku

Weapon: Red lightsaber

Height: 1.93 metres

Vehicle: Geonosian speeder, Geonosian Solar Sailor

Master: Darth Sidious

Count Dooku is a disillusioned former Jedi Master who lost faith in the Republic and abandoned the Jedi order. Dooku is a master in the old style of fencing and he wields his scimitar-handled lightsaber with skill and grace. After ten years in seclusion, Count Dooku has resurfaced as a Dark Lord of the Sith.

WELCOME TO THE

THE LIFE OF ANAKIN SKYWALKER / DARTH VADER

YEAR	AGE	EVENT
-42	0	Year of birth
-32	9	Wins Boonta Eve Classic
-32	9	Freed from slavery and leaves Shmi to become a Jedi
-32	9	Destroys droid control ship during the Battle of Naboo
-32	9	Death of Qui-Gon Jinn
-32	10	Turns 10 years old
-29	13	Constructs his own lightsaber
-22	20	Assigned to protect Padmé Amidala/ Goes to Naboo
-22	20	Returns to Tatooine
-22	20	Death of Shmi Skywalker
-22	20	Mission to Geonosis
-22	20	Loses arm druing battle with Count Dooku

SITH!

-22	20	Marries Padmé Amidala
-19	22	Becomes a Jedi Knight
-19	22	Last sees Padmé before embarking on the Outer Rim Sieges
-19	23	Battle of Coruscant
-19	23	Becomes Darth Vader
-19	23	Wipes out the Jedi at the Jedi Temple
-19	23	Wipes out the leaders of the Separatists
-19	23	Duel with Obi-Wan on Mustafar
-19	23	Given armour
-19	23	Luke and Leia born
0	42	Battle of Yavin
1	43	Learns that his son Luke Skywalker destroyed the Death Star
3	45	Confronts Luke Skywalker at Bespin
4	46	Sacrifices himself for Luke Skywalker
4	46	Becomes one with the Force

Published by Pedigree Books Limited
Beech Hill House, Walnut Gardens, Exeter, Devon EX4 4DH
E-mail books@pedigreegroup.co.uk
Published 2006

CONTENTS